Maths

How to use this book with your child:

It is recommended that an adult spends time with a child while doing any kind of school practice, to offer encouragement and guidance. Find a quiet place to work, preferably at a table, and encourage your child to hold his or her pen or pencil correctly.

Try to work at your child's pace and avoid spending too long on any one page or activity. Most of all, emphasise the fun element of what you are doing and enjoy this special and exciting time!

Don't forget to add your reward sticker to each page you complete!

Reward sticker!

Designed by Plum5
Illustrations by Sue King, Sharon Smart and Andy Geeson
Educational consultant Josh Levenson and Nina Filipek

www.autumnchildrensbooks.co.uk

Count to 100

What numbers are missing from this 100 square?
Fill in the missing numbers.

1	2	3	4	5	6	7	8	9	10
11	12	13	14	15	16	17	18	19	20
21	22	23	24	25	26	27	28	29	30
31	32	33	34	35	36	37	38	39	40
41	42	43	44	45	46	47	48	49	50
51	52	53	54	55	56	57	58	59	60
61	62	63	64	65	66	67	68	69	70
71	72	73	74	75	76	77	78	79	80
81	82	83	84	85	86	87	88	89	90
91	92	93	94	95	96	97	98	99	100

Well done!

Count in 2s, 5s and 10s

Help the three frogs get to their lilypads by writing in the missing numbers in these sequences.

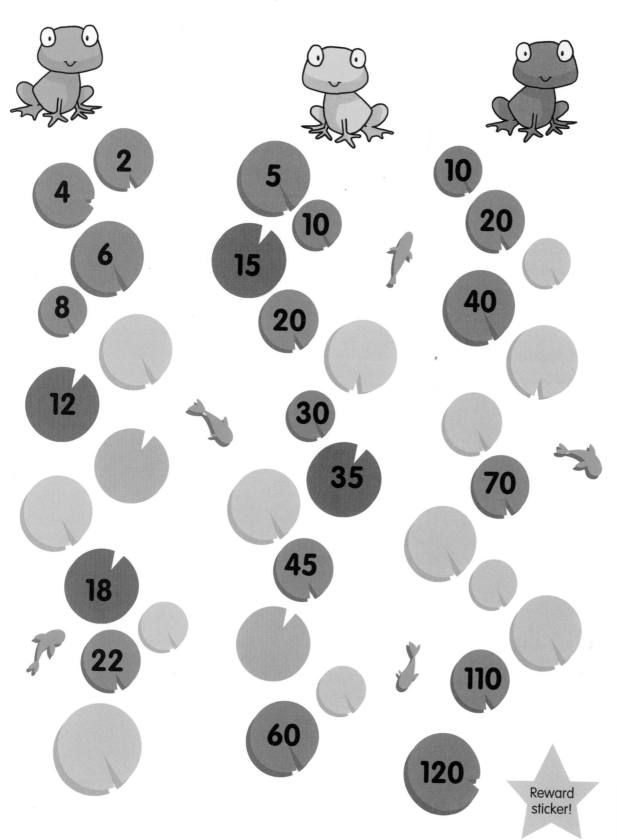

Reward sticker!

One more or less

Add one more or take one away.
Write the answers in the boxes.

e.g. **7 + 1 =** $\boxed{8}$ or **2 – 1 =** $\boxed{1}$

4 + 1 = ☐   **8 – 1 =** ☐

8 + 1 = ☐   **5 – 1 =** ☐

3 + 1 = ☐   **3 – 1 =** ☐

6 + 1 = ☐   **7 – 1 =** ☐

Reward
sticker!

Grouping

Put these bees into groups of 3.

How many groups are there?

How many bees are there altogether?

Put these sweets into groups of 4.

How many groups are there?

How many sweets are there altogether?

Adding up

Do the additions. Write the answers in the boxes.

$1 + 2 =$ ☐

$4 + 8 =$ ☐

$6 + 5 =$ ☐

$2 + 10 =$ ☐

$8 + 1 =$ ☐

$3 + 5 =$ ☐

$3 + 3 =$ ☐

$9 + 3 =$ ☐

$6 + 8 =$ ☐

$8 + 8 =$ ☐

$10 + 10 =$ ☐

$9 + 9 =$ ☐

Reward sticker!

12 + 4 = ☐   8 + 3 = ☐

4 + 4 = ☐   10 + 11 = ☐

2 + 12 = ☐   11 + 12 = ☐

4 + 5 = ☐   10 + 6 = ☐

14 + 3 = ☐   8 + 7 = ☐

9 + 8 = ☐   11 + 8 = ☐

16 + 4 = ☐   16 + 5 = ☐

Taking away

Do the subtractions. Write the answers in the boxes.

5 − 2 = ☐   7 − 2 = ☐

6 − 2 = ☐   13 − 12 = ☐

12 − 6 = ☐   20 − 11 = ☐

7 − 6 = ☐   18 − 9 = ☐

3 − 2 = ☐   16 − 14 = ☐

8 − 5 = ☐   4 − 2 = ☐

Reward sticker!

13 − 2 = ⬜

8 − 5 = ⬜

9 − 4 = ⬜

12 − 8 = ⬜

7 − 1 = ⬜

8 − 2 = ⬜

20 − 16 = ⬜

15 − 13 = ⬜

19 − 17 = ⬜

17 − 12 = ⬜

19 − 13 = ⬜

15 − 8 = ⬜

14 − 6 = ⬜

13 − 5 = ⬜

Reward sticker!

Fact families

Here is a fact family for 3 + 5 = 8.

- 3 + 5 = 8
- 8 − 5 = 3
- 5 + 3 = 8
- 8 − 3 = 5

Complete the following fact families.

- 2 + 5 = 7
- ___ − ___ = ___

- 5 + 2 = 7
- ___ − ___ = ___

- 3 + 4 = 7
- ___ − ___ = ___

- ___ + ___ = ___
- ___ − ___ = ___

- 1 + 8 = 9
- ___ − ___ = ___

- ___ + ___ = ___
- ___ − ___ = ___

Reward sticker!

Here is a fact family for 13 + 7 = 20.

- **13 + 7 = 20**   - **7 + 13 = 20**
- **20 − 7 = 13**   - **20 − 13 = 7**

Complete the following fact families.

- **14 + 6 = 20**   - ___ + ___ = ___

- ___ − ___ = ___   - ___ − ___ = ___

- **12 + 8 = 20**   - ___ + ___ = ___

- ___ − ___ = ___   - ___ − ___ = ___

- **17 + 3 = 20**   - ___ + ___ = ___

- ___ − ___ = ___   - ___ − ___ = ___

Missing numbers

Fill in the missing numbers to solve these out of this world addition and subtraction problems.

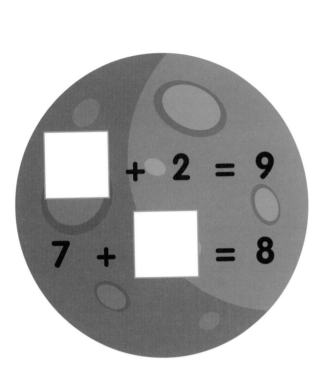

$\square + 2 = 9$

$7 + \square = 8$

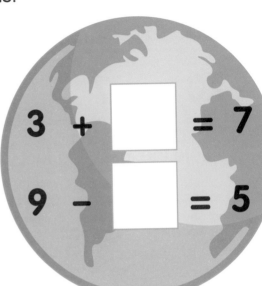

$3 + \square = 7$

$9 - \square = 5$

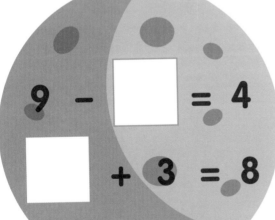

$9 - \square = 4$

$\square + 3 = 8$

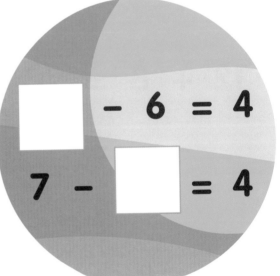

$\square - 6 = 4$

$7 - \square = 4$

Reward sticker!

☐ + 12 = 19

7 + ☐ = 15

3 + ☐ = 20

8 + ☐ = 17

☐ − 6 = 11

16 − ☐ = 11

19 − ☐ = 14

☐ + 3 = 18

Multiplying by 2

Complete this 2 times table grid. Write the answers in the boxes.

1 x 2 = ☐   7 x 2 = ☐

2 x 2 = ☐   8 x 2 = ☐

3 x 2 = ☐   9 x 2 = ☐

4 x 2 = ☐   10 x 2 = ☐

5 x 2 = ☐   11 x 2 = ☐

6 x 2 = ☐   12 x 2 = ☐

Reward sticker!

More multiplying by 2

Find the missing numbers for these 2 times table questions.
Write the answers in the boxes. We've done the first one for you!

$\boxed{3}$ × 2 = 6 $\boxed{}$ × 2 = 4

$\boxed{}$ × 2 = 16 $\boxed{}$ × 2 = 8

$\boxed{}$ × 2 = 20 $\boxed{}$ × 2 = 14

$\boxed{}$ × 2 = 18 $\boxed{}$ × 2 = 10

Reward
sticker!

Multiplying by 5

Complete this 5 times table grid. Write the answers in the boxes.

1 x 5 = ☐   7 x 5 = ☐

2 x 5 = ☐   8 x 5 = ☐

3 x 5 = ☐   9 x 5 = ☐

4 x 5 = ☐   10 x 5 = ☐

5 x 5 = ☐   11 x 5 = ☐

6 x 5 = ☐   12 x 5 = ☐

Reward sticker!

More multiplying by 5

Find the missing numbers for these 5 times table questions.
Write the answers in the boxes. We've done the first one for you!

| 3 | × 5 = 15 | | × 5 = 20 |

| | × 5 = 40 | | × 5 = 50 |

| | × 5 = 45 | | × 5 = 60 |

| | × 5 = 25 | | × 5 = 10 |

Reward sticker!

Multiplying by 10

Complete this 10 times table grid. Write the answers in the boxes.

1 x 10 = ☐   7 x 10 = ☐

2 x 10 = ☐   8 x 10 = ☐

3 x 10 = ☐   9 x 10 = ☐

4 x 10 = ☐   10 x 10 = ☐

5 x 10 = ☐   11 x 10 = ☐

6 x 10 = ☐   12 x 10 = ☐

Reward sticker!

More multiplying by 10

Find the missing numbers for these 10 times table questions.
Write the answers in the boxes. We've done the first one for you!

3 × 10 = 30 $\boxed{}$ × 10 = 50

$\boxed{}$ × 10 = 80 $\boxed{}$ × 10 = 40

$\boxed{}$ × 10 = 90 $\boxed{}$ × 10 = 60

$\boxed{}$ × 10 = 100 $\boxed{}$ × 10 = 70

Reward
sticker!

Double bubble

Double these numbers.
Hint: double 4 is the same as 4 + 4.

Double 4

Double 9

Double 7

Double 6

Double 5

Double 8

Reward sticker!

2D shapes

square   **rectangle**   **circle**   **triangle**

Count all the **squares**.
How many are there altogether?
Write your answer in the box.

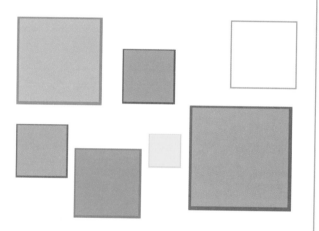

Count all the **rectangles**.
How many are there altogether?
Write your answer in the box.

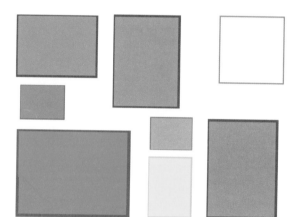

Count all the **circles**.
How many are there altogether?
Write your answer in the box.

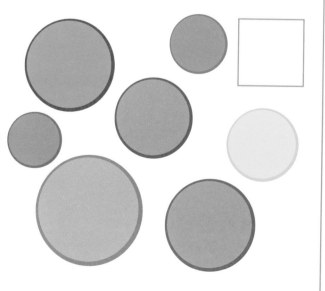

Count all the **triangles**.
How many are there altogether?
Write your answer in the box.

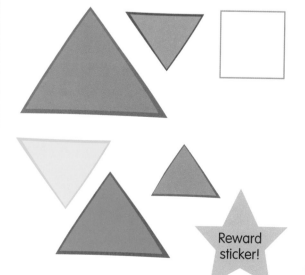

Reward sticker!

Halves

Shade in **half** of the following shapes. The first shape has been done for you.

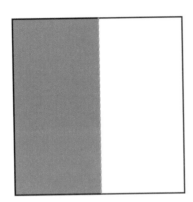

square

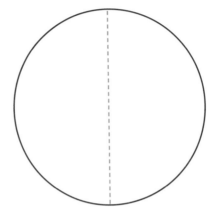

circle

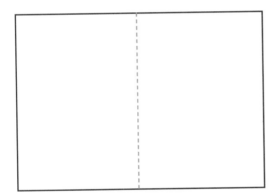

rectangle

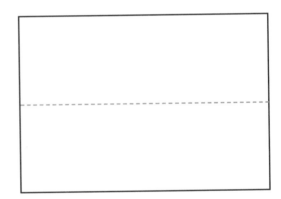

rectangle

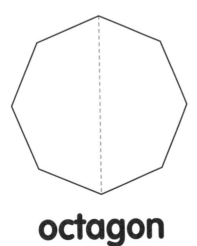

octagon

pentagon

Reward sticker!

Draw a ring around **half** of the objects for each question.
Then answer the questions and write your answer in the box.

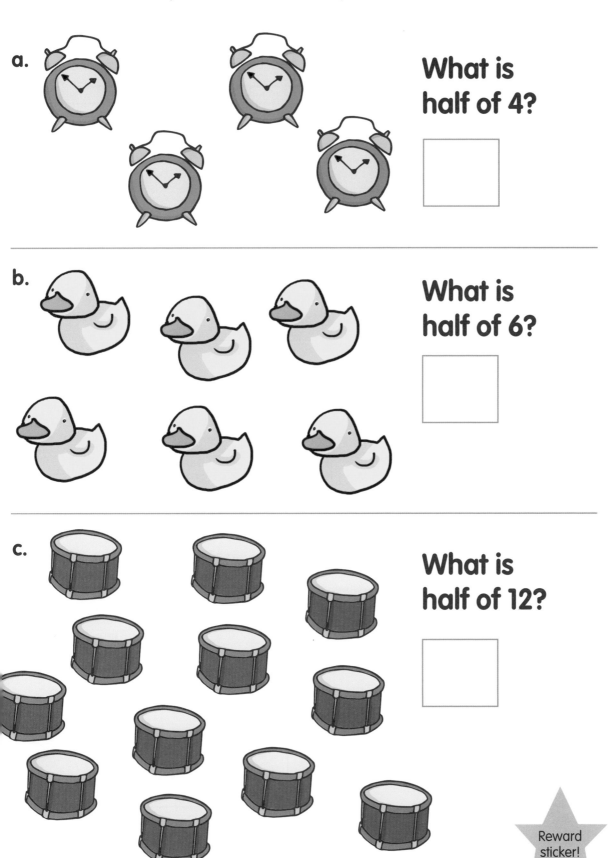

a.

What is half of 4?

b.

What is half of 6?

c.

What is half of 12?

Reward sticker!

Quarters

Shade in a **quarter** of the following shapes. Pick a different one each time. The first shape has been done for you!

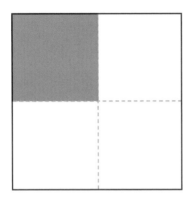

square

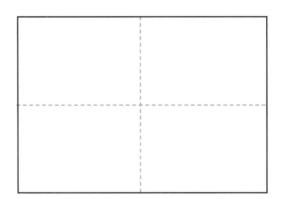

rectangle

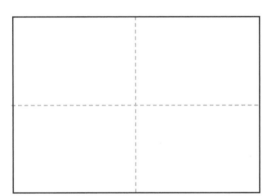

rectangle

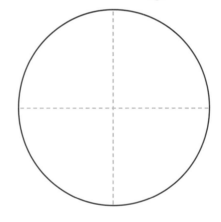

circle

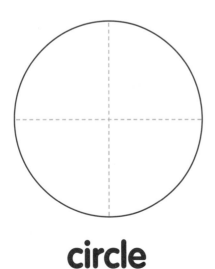

circle

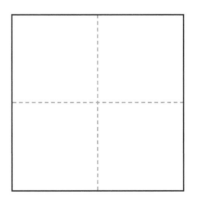

square

Reward sticker!

Draw a ring around a **quarter** of the objects for each question. Then answer the questions and write your answer in the box.

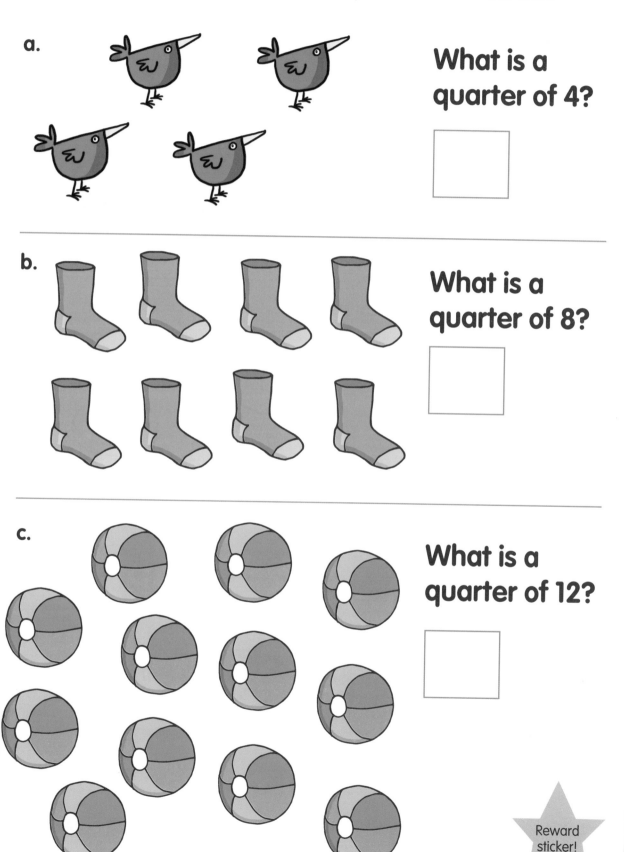

a. **What is a quarter of 4?**

b. **What is a quarter of 8?**

c. **What is a quarter of 12?**

Reward sticker!

Coins

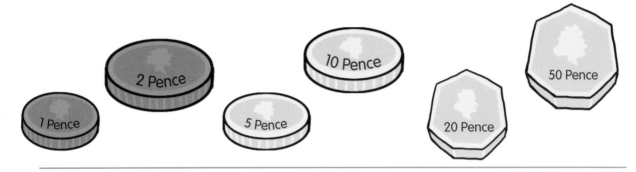

---

a. What two coins are these?

____ and ____

How much are they worth in total?

---

b. What two coins are these?

____ and ____

How much are they worth in total?

---

c. What two coins are these?

____ and ____

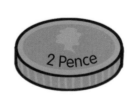

How much are they worth in total?

Reward sticker!

3D shapes

Complete the names of these 3D shapes by filling in the missing letters.

c__l__nde__

c o__ __

sp__ __re

c__ __oid

This is a face

Count all the faces on this cube.

How many faces does a cube have?

Colour by shapes

Follow the code to colour this picture.
Choose your own colours where there are no code symbols.

triangles	**circles**	**squares**	**stars**
▲	⬤	◼	★
light blue	light green	dark blue	dark green

Number patterns

Look carefully at each line of number patterns and fill in the missing numbers.

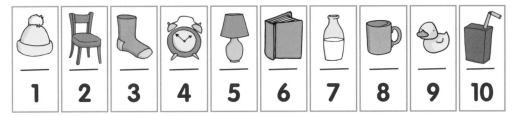

1 2 3 4 5 6 7 8 9 10

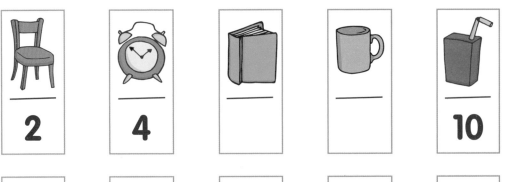

2 4 ___ ___ 10

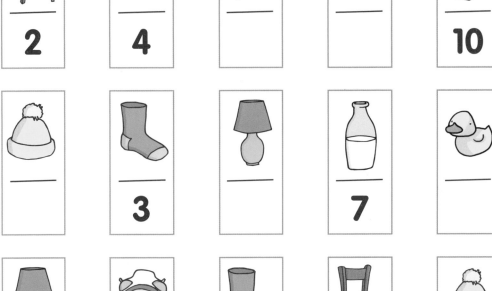

___ 3 ___ 7 ___

___ ___ 3 ___ 1

___ ___ 8 7 ___

Mental maths

Answer these questions in your head!
Write the answers in the boxes.

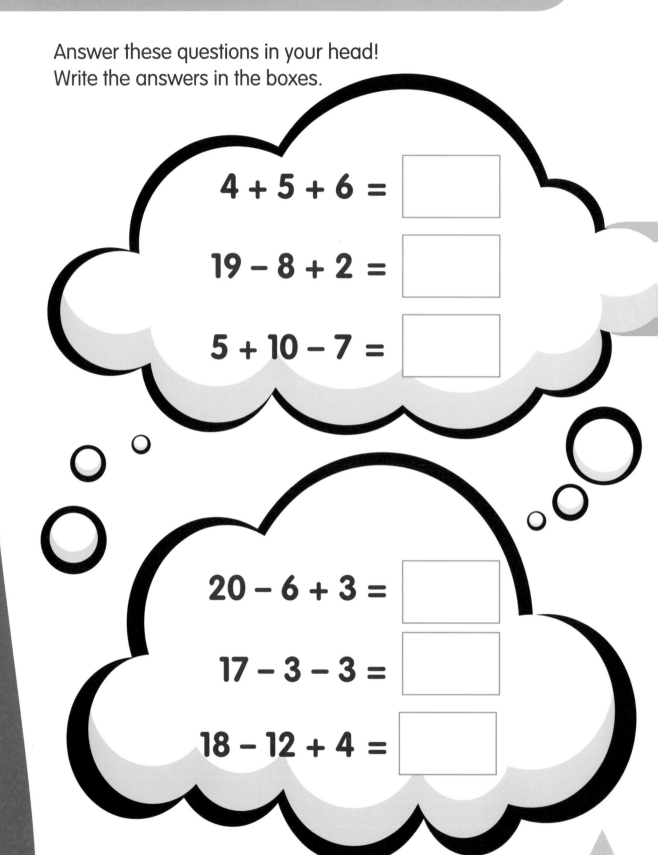

4 + 5 + 6 =

19 − 8 + 2 =

5 + 10 − 7 =

20 − 6 + 3 =

17 − 3 − 3 =

18 − 12 + 4 =

Reward sticker!

Answers

Count to 100

1	2	**3**	4	5	6	**7**	8	9	10
11	**12**	13	14	**15**	16	17	**18**	19	**20**
21	22	23	**24**	25	**26**	27	28	**29**	30
31	32	**33**	34	**35**	36	37	38	39	40
41	**42**	43	44	45	**46**	**47**	48	49	**50**
51	52	**53**	54	**55**	56	57	58	**59**	60
61	62	63	**64**	65	66	67	**68**	69	70
71	72	73	74	**75**	76	**77**	78	79	**80**
81	**82**	83	**84**	85	**86**	87	88	89	90
91	92	**93**	94	95	96	97	**98**	99	**100**

Count in 2s, 5s and 10s

2, 4, 6, 8, **10**, 12, **14**, **16**, 18, **20**, 22, **24**

5, 10, 15, 20, **25**, 30, 35, **40**, 45, **50**, **55**, 60

10, 20, **30**, 40, **50**, **60**, 70, **80**, **90**, **100**, 110, 120

One more or less

4 + 1 = **5**
8 + 1 = **9**
3 + 1 = **4**
6 + 1 = **7**
8 − 1 = **7**
5 − 1 = **4**
3 − 1 = **2**
7 − 1 = **6**

Grouping

5 groups of bees, 15 bees altogether
3 groups of sweets, 12 sweets altogether

Adding up

1 + 2 = **3**	4 + 8 = **12**
6 + 5 = **11**	2 + 10 = **12**
8 + 1 = **9**	3 + 5 = **8**
3 + 3 = **6**	9 + 3 = **12**
6 + 8 = **14**	8 + 8 = **16**
10 + 10 = **20**	9 + 9 = **18**

12 + 4 = **16**	8 + 3 = **11**
4 + 4 = **8**	10 + 11 = **21**
2 + 12 = **14**	11 + 12 = **23**
4 + 5 = **9**	10 + 6 = **16**
14 + 3 = **17**	8 + 7 = **15**
9 + 8 = **17**	11 + 8 = **19**
16 + 4 = **20**	16 + 5 = **21**

Taking away

5 − 2 = **3**	7 − 2 = **5**
6 − 2 = **4**	13 − 12 = **1**
12 − 6 = **6**	20 − 11 = **9**
7 − 6 = **1**	18 − 9 = **9**
3 − 2 = **1**	16 − 14 = **2**
8 − 5 = **3**	4 − 2 = **2**

13 − 2 = **11**	8 − 5 = **3**
9 − 4 = **5**	12 − 8 = **4**
7 − 1 = **6**	8 − 2 = **6**
20 − 16 = **4**	15 − 13 = **2**
19 − 17 = **2**	17 − 12 = **5**
19 − 13 = **6**	15 − 8 = **7**
14 − 6 = **8**	13 − 5 = **8**

Fact families

7 − 5 = 2, **7 − 2 = 5**,
4 + 3 = 7, **7 − 4 = 3**, **7 − 3 = 4**
8 + 1 = 9, **9 − 8 = 1**, **9 − 1 = 8**
6 + 14 = 20, **20 − 6 = 14**, **20 − 14 = 6**
8 + 12 = 20, **20 − 8 = 12**, **20 − 12 = 8**
3 + 17 = 20, **20 − 3 = 17**, **20 − 17 = 3**

Missing numbers

7 + 2 = 9	7 + **1** = 8
9 − **5** = 4	**5** + 3 = 8
3 + **4** = 7	9 − **4** = 5
10 − 6 = 4	7 − **3** = 4
7 + 12 = 19	7 + **8** = 15
3 + **17** = 20	8 + **9** = 17
19 − **5** = 14	**15** + 3 = 18
17 − 6 = 11	16 − **5** = 11

Multiplying by 2

1 x 2 = **2**	7 x 2 = **14**
2 x 2 = **4**	8 x 2 = **16**
3 x 2 = **6**	9 x 2 = **18**
4 x 2 = **8**	10 x 2 = **20**
5 x 2 = **10**	11 x 2 = **22**
6 x 2 = **12**	12 x 2 = **24**

Answers

More multiplying by 2

8	x	2	=	16	**2**	x 2	=	4
10	x	2	=	20	**4**	x 2	=	8
9	x	2	=	18	**7**	x 2	=	14
					5	x 2	=	10

Multiplying by 5

1 x 5 =	**5**		7 x 5 =	**35**
2 x 5 =	**10**		8 x 5 =	**40**
3 x 5 =	**15**		9 x 5 =	**45**
4 x 5 =	**20**		10 x 5 =	**50**
5 x 5 =	**25**		11 x 5 =	**55**
6 x 5 =	**30**		12 x 5 =	**60**

More multiplying by 5

8 x 5 = 40		**4** x 5 = 20
9 x 5 = 45		**10** x 5 = 50
5 x 2 = 25		**12** x 5 = 60
		2 x 5 = 10

Multiplying by 10

1 x 10 =	**10**		7 x 10 =	**70**
2 x 10 =	**20**		8 x 10 =	**80**
3 x 10 =	**30**		9 x 10 =	**90**
4 x 10 =	**40**		10 x 10 =	**100**
5 x 10 =	**50**		11 x 10 =	**110**
6 x 10 =	**60**		12 x 10 =	**120**

More multiplying by 10

8 x 10 = 80		**5** x 10 = 50
9 x 10 = 90		**4** x 10 = 40
10 x 10 = 100		**6** x 10 = 60
		7 x 10 = 70

Double bubble

Double 4 = **8**
Double 9 = **18**
Double 7 = **14**
Double 6 = **12**
Double 5 = **10**
Double 8 = **16**

2D Shapes

6 squares   7 rectangles
7 circles   5 triangles

Halves

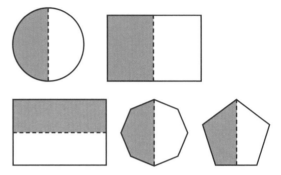

a. 2 **b.** 3 **c.** 6

Quarters

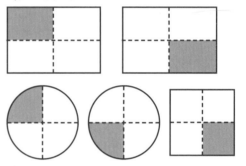

a. 1 **b.** 2 **c.** 3

Coins

a. 1p + 10p = 11p
b. 20p + 5p = 25p
c. 2p + 50p = 52p

3D shapes

cylinder   cone
sphere   cuboid

The cube has 6 faces.

Number patterns

2, 4, **6**, **8**,10
1, 3, **5**, 7, **9**
5, **4**, 3, **2**, 1
10, **9**, 8, 7, **6**

Mental maths

4 + 5 + 6 = **15**		19 − 8 + 2 = **13**
5 +10 − 7 = **8**		20 − 6 + 3 = **17**
17 − 3 − 3 = **11**		18 − 12 + 4 = **10**